201
weird true facts

WTF

[science]

harry bright & jakob anser

MJF BOOKS

New York

Published by MJF Books
Fine Communications
322 Eighth Avenue
New York, NY 10001

WTF *(science)*
LC Control Number: 2015909757
ISBN 978-1-60671-313-6

Printed in the United States of America.

Designed by Lisa Chovnick

Images: Clipart.com, Wikimedia Commons,
iStock.com, and NASA

MJF Books and the MJF colophon are trademarks
of Fine Creative Media, Inc.

QF   10   9   8   7   6   5   4   3   2

201
weird true facts

WTF

[science]

Which came first, the chicken or the egg? The chicken. The protein necessary to produce eggshells originates in the ovaries of a hen.

In 2015 scientists successfully unboiled eggs, returning solid whites to their liquid state.

Scientists are capable of mind control. In an experiment reminiscent of the memory manipulation performed in the film *The Eternal Sunshine of the Spotless Mind*, scientists stimulated the brains of sleeping mice to evoke positive associations for a particular location. When the mice awoke, they made a beeline for this happy place.

S cientists have discovered an on/off switch for thirst. When CAMK11 neurons are activated in mice, the mice seek water whether they're thirsty or not. If the corresponding VGAT neurons are turned on, they'll stop drinking even if they're dehydrated and actually dying of thirst.

There are more atoms in a teaspoonful of water than there are teaspoonfuls of water in the Atlantic Ocean.

WTF
science

ICICLES CAN FORM UNDERWATER. Stalactite-shaped *brinicles,* or brine icicles, form beneath sea ice when columns of super-cold, super-salty water plunge down into the unfrozen seawater below. Under the right conditions, these ice fingers can reach the sea floor and flash-freeze everything in their path.

Killer whales undergo menopause. Post-menopausal matriarch killer whales become pod leaders.

Killer whales are also capable of learning the language of the bottlenose dolphin.

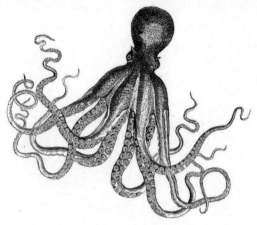

If the colossal squid, *Mesonychoteuthis hamiltoni,* tries to swallow too big a bite, it risks brain damage. This giant sea creature's brain is doughnut-shaped, and its esophagus runs right through the doughnut hole. The chances of this happening are slim, because colossal squid—which can survive on just one ounce of food per day—tear their prey into tiny pieces.

WTF
science

Ming the Clam was 507 years old, the oldest living animal in the world—that is, until scientists accidentally killed him while trying to figure out his age.

Cuttlefish can change color and even pattern through manipulations of their nervous system. This allows them to put on a psychedelic light show to hypnotize prey before snatching it with their tentacles.

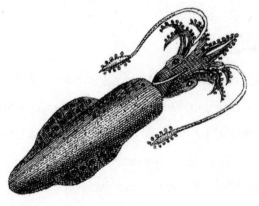

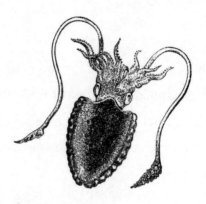

Cuttlefish are also experts at sending out mixed signals. During courtship, a male cuttlefish flashes its psychedelic display to attract a female. If another male happens by, the courting cuttlefish will confine the visuals to one side of his body, turning off the lights on the side facing the rival, as if to say, "Nothing to see here, pal."

T*urritopsis dohrnii,* a small, bell-shaped jellyfish native to the Mediterranean Sea, is the only animal capable of reverting to an earlier developmental stage. This process of transdifferentiation of older cells into new cells can theoretically go on forever, which explains why this tiny creature is called the immortal jellyfish.

The male platypus has a spur on each hind foot loaded with venom that is strong enough to kill a dog.

EARLY MAN'S BEST FRIEND. According to anthropologist Dr. Pat Shipman, the alliance between modern humans and tamed wolves finished off Neanderthals and their cousins. In a typical hunt, domesticated wolves chased down the prey, while humans armed with spears conserved energy and focused on the kill. These symbiotic, food-sharing apex predators eventually outcompeted all rivals.

Archaeologists digging in the Denisova Cave in Siberia stumbled upon a pinkie bone fragment and some bearlike teeth belonging to a previously unknown hominid species that split off from Neanderthals around 400,000 years ago. Analysis of the Denisovan nuclear genome showed that the partial pinkie came from an eight-year-old girl with brown hair, brown eyes, and dark skin.

A team of cardiologists gave 137 mummies from four ancient populations CAT scans to look for atherosclerosis, a precursor to heart attack or stroke. To their surprise, 34 percent of their "patients" had calcified plaque buildup on their arterial walls, about the same level as is found in modern populations.

TELESCOPES ARE TIME MACHINES. Using the Hubble Space Telescope, astronomers are watching reruns of the same nine-billion-year-old supernova explosion. The gravity from a cluster of distant galaxies bent and magnified the exploding star's light rays, broadcasting multiple images of the same event.

———

Engineers have developed telescopic contact lenses. A view of 2.8× magnification can be activated with a wink.

Scallops can have up to 100 eyes—amazing when you consider that they don't have brains.

The Philippine tarsier, a tiny primate found only in Southeast Asia, has the largest eyes relative to body size of all mammals. Each eye weighs more than its brain.

THE EYES HAVE IT. When you slice an onion, a chemical reaction releases a volatile sulfuric gas called syn-propanethial S-oxide. When mixed with tears, the gas creates sulfuric acid, which is why your eyes burn. This lacrimatory factor is the onion's way of warding off predators.

Wwhat do an onion, a broad-footed salamander, and the African lungfish have in common? They all have larger genomes than humans. They have 5, 20, and 41 times more, respectively, than the 3.2 billion DNA base pairs in the human genome.

A flowering plant called *Paris japonica* has the largest genome yet discovered. With 149 billion base pairs, the DNA from a single cell would stretch the length of a football field, from one goalpost to the other.

———————

The average human baby is born with 60 new genetic mutations.

Children who consume peanut butter from infancy (starting at 4 to 11 months of age) at a rate of about four teaspoons per week are 80 percent less likely to develop a peanut allergy by their fifth birthday than their non-peanut-eating peers.

If you're allergic to lobster, crab, or shrimp, you may also be allergic to dust mites. As arthropods, they're closely related.

The wasp *Rostropria garbo* is named for Greta Garbo because, unlike most colony insects, it likes to be alone.

B*revisana brevis,* an African cicada, is the loudest insect in the world. At 106.7 decibels, its distress call is as loud as some home burglar alarms.

Beetles account for one-quarter of all animals on Earth. There are roughly 5,400 known species of mammals, 27,000 species of fish, even 15,000 species of roundworms, but there are 350,000 species of beetles—and counting.

Birds can count and make maps. In late summer and fall, the Clark's nutcracker buries tens of thousands of nutritious pine seeds in thousands of tiny caches, the precise locations of which it recalls throughout the winter.

The crow may be as clever at making and using simple tools with its beak as a chimpanzee is with its hands. Crows can make hooks out of wire, whittle sticks, and use analogical reasoning to modify tools for new purposes.

The rook, a member of the crow family, has also exhibited tool-making capabilities—but only under scientific observation. In the wild, rooks are likelier to follow the path of least resistance, making it the rare species that *can* use tools but doesn't.

Bowerbirds are the romantic architects of the animal kingdom. To woo mates, males build intricate bowers and decorate them, often with bright or shiny items, such as beetle carapaces, colorful mushrooms, and even shell casings and colored plastic. They will also make attractive flower arrangements, and then toss them out when they begin to wilt—which makes bowerbirds one of the only species besides humans to use plants for decoration rather than consumption.

RED VELVET MITES ARE SPERM ARTISTS. When it's time to mate, the male constructs a "love garden" using leaves, twigs, and droplets of sperm deposited on tiny stalks. When he's done, he lays down a long and winding road of sperm leading to his love garden, and if a female is sufficiently impressed, she'll seek out the garden and sit in the sperm. But if a rival is the first to find the trail, he'll destroy the love garden and build his own in the same spot.

People of Chhattisgarh, a state in central India, use oil extracted from the red velvet mite as an aphrodisiac. It has been nicknamed Indian Viagra.

Studies show that when the weather is cold, American women who are ovulating tend to wear pink or red clothing. Women who are *not* ovulating are attracted to men who exhibit nonverbal expressions of shame.

When it comes to initial sexual attraction, according to a team of psychologists from the University of British Columbia, women prefer men who are either powerful or moody. Men, on the other hand, are most attracted to happy, smiling women and least attracted to women who are proud and confident.

Side-blotched lizards come in three different color versions, or "morphs." The three morphs have different, but equally successful, mating strategies that play out like a courtship version of rock-paper-scissors. Orange-throated males (scissors) are aggressive and cut out blue-throated males (paper), which prefer to stand guard over their mates. Yellow-throated males (rock), who sneak onto other males' turf, often by acting like females, are put under wraps by the protective blue-throats (paper) but successfully crush the roving orange-throated males (scissors).

Like lizards, some scorpions can sacrifice their tails as a last-ditch defense mechanism. Unlike lizards, however, they can't grow them back. Even more unfortunate, a scorpion's anus is located at the end of the tail, so a scorpion with a severed tail can't expel waste. It can survive another eight months before dying of fecal contamination.

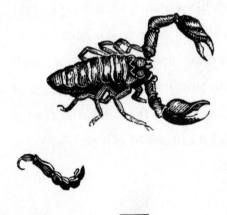

The southern gastric-brooding frog, discovered in Australia in 1972 and extinct by 1983, would swallow its fertilized eggs and use its stomach like a uterus, something no other animal has been known to do. The eggs developed into tadpoles and eventually little frogs in this stomach-uterus. When the mother could no longer keep them down she would orally expel the brood of as many as 25 baby frogs.

L IZARD SPIT CURBS YOUR APPETITE. Exendin-4, a hormone found in the saliva of Gila monsters, reduces hunger pangs in humans by stimulating the "reward" and "motivation" regions of the brain.

When you get goose bumps while listening to music, your brain has just been flooded with dopamine, the neurotransmitter that controls the brain's pleasure center.

Humans are hardwired to care about other people. In studies of the human brain, MRI scans show that the periaqueductal gray area, a very old brain structure common among mammals, lights up when subjects are shown pictures of suffering. These images also activate the vagus nerve, which conveys "gut feelings" to the brain.

A recent study at Oregon State University found that high levels of xanthohumol, a type of flavonoid found in hops, improved cognitive function in young mice. The researchers cautioned, however, that a human would need to down about 4,225 pints of beer a day to reach the xanthohumol levels used in the study.

THERE ONCE WAS A GUINEA PIG AS BIG AS A BUFFALO. Some three million years ago, *Josephoartigasia monesi,* an evolutionary cousin of today's cuddly guinea pig, roamed the South American coast. It weighed more than a ton and is believed to have used its overgrown incisors the same way an elephant uses its tusks.

Tickling a rat will make it laugh. Like humans, some rats like to be tickled and some don't. Those that do are optimistic, expecting reward rather than punishment. Those that don't like to be tickled tend to be anxious and neurotic.

If a man's ring finger is longer than his index finger, he was exposed to a higher than usual amount of testosterone in utero during the second trimester.

Men with long right ring fingers are risk-takers who are more promiscuous, more verbally aggressive, and better at sports than those with shorter ring fingers. Women with this "man hands" finger ratio are more likely to have a good sense of direction.

Without any landmarks or recognizable celestial orientation points, humans are wired to walk in circles.

———

Until recently it was believed that only birds, seals, and humans looked to the stars for orientation, but it turns out African dung beetles use the sky to navigate away from the communal dung pile. They orient not to individual stars but to the entire Milky Way.

Every time you look at the moon, you're looking one second into the past.

Every sunrise is a mirage. As the sun rises, air in Earth's atmosphere bends its image upward, so we see the sun two minutes before it actually breaks the horizon.

There are more atoms in the average adult human body than there are stars in the observable universe.

———————

If you took the space out of matter, every human on the planet could fit inside an apple—impossible, of course, because without space, apples would be smaller than molecules.

It snows carbon dioxide on Mars and rains heavy metal on Venus. Some planetary scientists believe it may rain diamonds on Jupiter and Saturn.

Because of the low gravity and thick atmosphere on Titan, Saturn's sixth moon, if you were to strap wings to your arms, you could fly over the lakes of ethane, methane, and propane that dot its surface with no more effort than it takes to walk.

The largest known storm is Jupiter's Great Red Spot—a sort of hurricane that has churned for more than 400 years.

The scent in the air during a thunderstorm is ozone. Some people think ozone smells like burnt wires or sparks, such as those made by old-time bumper cars.

The fresh, earthy smell after a light rain is called *petrichor,* from *petros,* meaning "stone," and *ichor,* the fluid that flows through the veins of the Greek gods of mythology. Light rain, this etymology suggests, smells like the blood of the gods spilling onto the stony ground.

Petrichor is actually the smell of oils released from dried plant matter and *geosmin,* an organic compound produced by soil-dwelling bacteria. When raindrops hit the ground, they capture the plant oils and earthy geosmin as aerosols, which then burst—much like bubbles in Champagne.

RAINDROPS AREN'T SHAPED LIKE TEARDROPS. Small raindrops, with a radius of one millimeter or less, are spherical. Medium-size raindrops flatten out, and look sort of like hamburger buns. And large raindrops, roughly five millimeters in radius, are two blobs with an arched connection in the middle, like a pair of headphones.

———————

The typical cumulus cloud holds about 550 tons of rainwater, or roughly the weight of 14,500 cats and dogs.

57
WTF
science

If you've ever passed out after bingeing on animal crackers, you may be suffering from gut fermentation syndrome. Also called "auto-brewery," this rare disorder causes carbohydrates in your intestines to ferment, producing ethanol as a byproduct. The ethanol is then absorbed into the bloodstream, which makes you drunk.

About ten million years ago, a genetic mutation of the enzymes in the tongue, throat, and stomach allowed our human ancestors to develop a tolerance to alcohol. As primates shifted from tree dwelling to a terrestrial style of life, the capacity to break down the ethanol found in rotting or fermented fruit on the forest floor became useful when other food was scarce.

P*roof* is the measure of alcohol in beverages. This use of the term originated in the sixteenth century when governments needed a way to "prove" the quantity of alcohol in a beverage in order to calculate its tax. This was done by soaking a gunpowder pellet in the liquid and then trying to light the pellet. If it ignited, the liquor was considered "above proof" and taxed at a higher rate than liquor that wouldn't ignite.

———————

A team of Mexican scientists turned tequila into synthetic diamonds.

Everyone knows you should eat plenty of fruit. But did you know you can also eat the stickers? Produce stickers are made from edible paper, and the U.S. Food and Drug Administration considers even the glue to be "food grade."

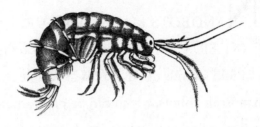

A sugary compound called chitin found in the exoskeletons of shrimp may soon replace semiconductors in nanostructured solar cells. Scientists can synthesize chitin into carbon quantum dots, spherical nanoparticles just 10 billionths of a meter thick, and then paint them over nanorods. While not yet as efficient as silicon-based materials, chitin is 50 times cheaper and is a sustainable resource.

Nanobots may soon cure cancer. With "DNA origami," researchers can fold strands of DNA into injectable nanoscale robots, which can be programmed to deliver a payload of drugs to destroy cancer cells while leaving nearby healthy tissue untouched.

———

DNA may soon be the next data storage medium. Just one gram of DNA can hold 455 exabytes of data. That's at least 225,000 times all the printed, video, and audio material held in the Library of Congress.

DNA-origami robots can perform logic operations just as a silicon-based computer can. A syringe containing one trillion of these 50-nanometer biocomputers has the processing power of an 8-bit Commodore 64.

The Commodore 64, which started volume production in early 1982, is still the best-selling computer model of all time, according to *Guinness World Records*.

When Dr. Irene Pepperberg's African gray parrot, Alex, saw his reflection in a mirror and asked, "What color?" he may have been the first nonhuman to ask an existential question.

How Much Does Flight Weigh?

The force of a downstroke made by a bird's wings is twice the weight of the bird.

Drunk birds sing like drunks. When scientists raised finches' blood alcohol level to between .05 and .08 percent, the tipsy birds began to slur their melodies.

Sober zebrafish will follow drunk zebrafish. The inebriated fish swim faster and more erratically than usual, which clearheaded fish perceive as boldness.

Zebrafish embryos, larvae, and now genetically modified adults are completely transparent, allowing researchers to see what's going on inside them. Researchers in Japan even captured a zebrafish's "thoughts" on video. (It was thinking about food.)

Fish INVENTED SEX. Fossils of
Microbrachius dicki, which lived 385 million
years ago, clearly show unique male and female
sex organs—the first ones known. The armor-
plated, jawed fish mated side by side, with their
armlike fins intertwined, as if they were square
dancing.

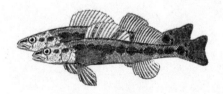

The pacu is a South American freshwater fish with teeth like those of humans. It uses its choppers to crush nuts and fruits fallen from trees. There have been several reports of pacu mistaking the testicles of male swimmers for floating nuts.

For every human killed by a shark, approximately 10 million sharks are killed by humans.

Pestalotiopsis microspora, a fungus discovered in the Ecuadorian rain forest, is the only known microbe that can live on polyurethane, one of the most common plastics, in an anaerobic environment. This makes it a promising candidate for reducing waste in the oxygen-deprived depths of landfills.

Algae produce between 70 and 80 percent of the world's oxygen.

Petroleum occurs naturally from the decomposition over millions of years of algae, phytoplankton, and other small marine organisms.

Using a process called hydrothermal liquefaction, scientists can turn algae into crude oil in about an hour.

The *Brontosaurus,* a diplodocid first described by paleontologist Othniel Charles Marsh in 1877, did not technically exist until 2015. Marsh erroneously proclaimed the genus in a rush to one-up his rival, Edward Drinker Cope, during the late nineteenth century in what came to be known as the Bone Wars. In 1903 Marsh's bronto bones were said to have come from an *Apatosaurus.* But in 2015 scientists analyzed high-resolution scans of every diplodocid bone ever unearthed, and found notable differences between the *Apatosaurus* and the *Brontosaurus—* enough to reinstate this gigantic dinosaur with the high, narrow neck.

Usain Bolt has been clocked at a top speed of 27.44 miles per hour, making him one of the few humans who could have outrun a *Tyrannosaurus rex*. Computer models suggest the *T. rex* ran up to 25 miles per hour—meaning, everybody but world-class sprinters would end up as lunch.

Earth has had numerous extinction events, five of them major. The Permian-Triassic extinction, which occurred about 250 million years ago, resulted in a marine species loss of 96 percent and land species loss of 70 percent. The most recent extinction event was the K-Pg, which occurred about 65 million years ago and wiped out nearly all the dinosaurs.

All the matter we've ever observed with our increasingly powerful telescopes and computers makes up less than 5 percent of the universe. The rest is dark energy (68 percent) and dark matter (27 percent). Although we still don't know what dark matter is, it may have caused Earth's extinction events. Mass extinctions have occurred roughly 30 million years apart—about the frequency at which the Milky Way crosses the galactic plane. Some scientists hypothesize that clouds of dark matter could pull comets into Earth's orbit and also cause supervolcanic eruptions.

Sharks have been around longer than trees. *Archaeopteris*, among the earliest tree species, grew in what is now the Sahara Desert over 350 million years ago, but sharks have been around for 450 million years and have lived through all five mass extinction events.

The tardigrade, a water-dwelling microanimal known as the "slow walker" or "water bear," has also survived all five mass extinction events. An extremophile, it can endure just about any inhospitable environment by shriveling up into a dormant state and reviving when conditions improve, a process called cryptobiosis. In its desiccated state, it can endure temperatures from close to absolute zero to 300 degrees Fahrenheit. It can even withstand 1,000 times the radiation that would kill a rhino.

Tardigrades are the first animals to survive the vacuum of outer space. In 2007, the European Space Agency launched the Tardigrades in Space experiment (TARDIS), in which tardigrades were exposed to interstellar space and cosmic radiation for 12 days. That the tardigrades survived lends credence to the panspermia hypothesis: the idea that life was planted throughout the universe via space debris like comets and meteors.

Some NASA scientists believe that the first form of extraterrestrial intelligent life we encounter will be not little green men but superintelligent robots.

All the planets in our solar system would fit between the Earth and the moon with about 2,700 miles to spare.

From its discovery as a planet in 1930 to its demotion to dwarf planet in 2006, Pluto didn't make a single orbit. Pluto takes 248 Earth years to complete its revolution around the sun.

A total solar eclipse is possible only because the moon is 400 times smaller than the sun and also 400 times closer to Earth.

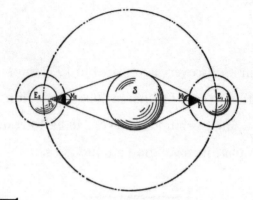

The moon is currently moving away from Earth at a rate of 1.5 inches a year. In roughly 563 million years, Earth will experience its final total solar eclipse, because the moon will appear too small to cover the sun.

Recent study: there are too many studies. The authors of *Attention Decay in Science* conclude that the decreasing rate of citations of recently published work is directly related to the exponential growth in the number of studies and the finite ability of scholars to keep up with them.

From the perspective of the mother's immune system, a fetus is a giant parasite. Recent research shows that both mouse and human sperm contains CD38, a molecule that plays a pivotal role in establishing maternal immune tolerance of the fetus by stimulating the mother to produce tolerogenic cells.

Even after they've given birth, mothers often feel as if their children are a physical part of them. This is true: In a phenomenon known as fetomaternal microchimerism, a fetus can leave behind cells that linger in the mother's body for up to 38 years after the pregnancy.

Microchimerism can also work the other way around. Cells with the mother's complete genome have been found in offspring well into their 20s.

———————

In humans, chimerism on a large scale occurs when you are both yourself and your twin. Fraternal twins have different DNA, so if one vanishes in the womb during gestation, the remaining fetus can absorb its DNA, resulting in a genetic chimera.

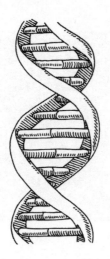

We all have webbed hands and feet in utero. We lose the webbing in the first trimester through apoptosis, or programmed cell death. The genetic protein responsible for this speedy web loss is called *sonic hedgehog,* named after Sega's video game character Sonic the Hedgehog.

89
WTF
science

In 1956, IBM launched the 305 RAMAC—"random-access method of accounting and control"—the first commercially successful computer with a hard-disk drive. It came in a cabinet as large as two refrigerators, weighed a ton, and stored 4.4 megabytes of data, or the equivalent of a four-minute pop song.

A computer program recently spat out a *partial* mathematical proof of the Erdős discrepancy problem; the partial proof contained 13 gigabytes of data—that's the equivalent of nearly 4,000 copies of *War and Peace,* and too long for any human to parse.

———————

Ada Lovelace, the daughter of Lord Byron, has been called the first computer programmer because of an algorithm she wrote in 1843 that calculates Bernoulli numbers. This code, considered the first computer program, was never used because it required a machine that was never built.

Physician Elena Bodnar, originally from Ukraine, won the 2009 Ig Nobel Prize in Public Health for inventing the Emergency Bra. Inspired by the Chernobyl nuclear disaster, Bodnar's invention doubles as two emergency face masks.

THE UNITED STATES GOVERNMENT NEARLY NUKED THE MOON. Project A119, a top-secret U.S. Air Force plan developed in 1958, called for the detonation of a nuclear bomb on the lunar surface to test mysteries about planetary astronomy. But it was also thought that a bright lunar flash would boost American morale after the Soviets took the lead in the space race.

On March 17, 2013, a meteorite the size of a small boulder traveling at 56,000 mph crashed into the moon. The impact generated a bright flash visible to the naked eye—but no one saw it. It was recorded by NASA's Lunar Impact Monitoring Program, which has the moon under constant surveillance.

The moon's gravitational pull is what creates high tides. Without the moon, we'd still have tides; they'd just be half as high. The sun's tidal effect is about half as strong as the moon's.

Galileo did not drop objects off the Leaning Tower of Pisa. Nevertheless, his *thought experiments* showed that terminal velocity—when the gravitational force pulling down on an object equals the aerodynamic drag force pushing up—is the same for all objects in a state of free fall, regardless of their mass.

If two solid spheres of different sizes and the same density are dropped into *water,* the larger one will hit bottom first.

———————

Virtually every galaxy in the universe, including our own Milky Way, has a super-massive black hole at its center, much like the nucleus of an atom.

The photon sphere is a region of space outside the event horizon of a black hole, where gravity is strong enough to force photons to travel in orbits. If you could somehow stand on the edge of the photon sphere and look straight ahead, you would see the back of your own head.

In a remote galaxy called PG 1302-102, two black holes are on a collision path. When they collide, which scientists say will happen in a million years, the impact will release an amount of energy equal to 100 million supernovas.

The total energy output of one supernova is equivalent to the total energy output of our sun during its 10-billion-year lifetime.

———————

Seventy thousand years ago, a small star passed within a light-year of the sun—the closest a star has been known to venture inside our solar system. Any comets that the star's gravitation may have pulled toward Earth won't arrive for another few hundred thousand years.

If you hold a steady speed through turn three of the Daytona International Speedway, you're accelerating. Acceleration is a change in velocity, and velocity is the rate at which an object changes its position.

SPACE SMELLS LIKE A NASCAR RACE.
The combustion of dying stars releases polycyclic
aromatic hydrocarbons, which smell like a
combination of hot metal, diesel fumes, and
barbecue. (Too bad you can't burp in space.)

You can't smell anything in space because
it's a vacuum. But astronauts coming in from
spacewalks outside the International Space
Station say their life suits smell like "fried steak."

Trimethylaminuria, commonly known as fish odor syndrome, is a rare inherited disorder that makes your urine, breath, and sweat smell like rotting fish.

If you happen upon something that looks like a six-tentacled octopus and smells like rotting flesh, you've probably come across *Clathrus archeri,* a fungus native to Australia and Tasmania commonly known as "octopus stinkhorn" or "devil's finger." When it first emerges from the ground, the limbs are ashen white and resemble a corpse's hand. As the fungus matures, the "tentacles" turn red. The foul odor attracts spore-dispersing flies, allowing the fungus to propagate.

Trained dogs can smell thyroid cancer in your urine. They can also smell breast and lung cancer on your breath.

Dogs understand human speech. Just like people, dogs interpret sounds that form words with the left hemisphere of their brains and, with the right, other sounds that convey a speaker's emotions or gender (things like intonation and emphasis). Scientists discovered this by studying which way dogs cocked their heads as they listened to different kinds of speech.

Imagination and reality flow in opposite directions in your brain.

Sphenopalatine ganglioneuralgia is the scientific name for brain freeze. It's your brain's mechanism for protecting itself from potentially damaging temperature change by telling you to slow down.

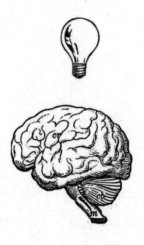

The human brain runs on 20 watts, just enough energy to power a dim light bulb.

You can use urine to charge your cellphone.
You can also use urine to grow new teeth.

You make better decisions when you have to pee. Bladder control has a spillover effect into other areas of impulse control, such as delaying instant gratification for longer-term reward. So to avoid an interminable Monday-morning meeting, fill everyone's cup with water and lock the conference room doors—the meeting will be shorter and you'll make better decisions.

BEDPANNING FOR GOLD? Medieval alchemists long dreamed of transforming lead into gold. It turns out you can get gold from human waste. In a city of a million people, sewage sludge, the semisolid byproduct of waste treatment facilities, contains up to $13 million-worth of metals, including several million dollars' worth of silver and gold.

Earthquakes turn water into gold.

A coal seam 90 feet below the surface of Australia's Mount Wingen has been burning for 5,500 years, making it the longest continuous fire on Earth.

DNA extracted from herring sperm can fireproof cotton.

Herring communicate by farting. They squeak out a high-pitched 22 kHz sound when they emit bubbles from their anus.

As an April Fools' Day joke in 1999, *Red Herring* magazine ran an article about a revolutionary new technology that allowed people to compose and send email telepathically. The hoax is tame by today's standards, given that German engineers hooked up a brain scanner to steering controls back in 2011 to develop the first thought-driven car.

In 2015, as part of an experimental Pentagon robotics program, a 55-year-old quadriplegic flew an F-35 simulator using nothing but her thoughts.

Seventy-five scientists recently signed a statement saying that commercial brain games don't improve cognitive functioning. Their advice? Aerobic exercise.

If you're feeling stupid, you might just have a virus—more specifically, the ATCV-1 chlorovirus, which until recently was thought to affect only green algae. Subjects whose throat swabs tested positive for ATCV-1 had shorter attention spans and processed visual information 10 percent more slowly than those who tested negative.

Viruses can get other viruses.

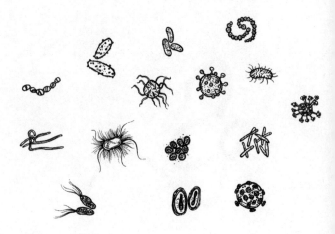

The New York City subway system is home to 637 unknown organisms. Researchers have discovered traces of drug-resistant and disease-causing bacteria, as well as fragments of anthrax and bubonic plague DNA.

A bubo is a swelling of a lymph node. Victims of bubonic plague get buboes in the neck, armpits, or groin.

———————

Lactobacilli are probiotics commonly found in yogurt. They are also the most prevalent bacteria found in a healthy vagina.

The collective genome of all the bacteria living in your gut is at least 150 times larger than your own genome.

———————————————

New research suggests bacteria, long thought to be clones, are unique social creatures that display sophisticated group dynamics. When two closely related groups compete for the same habitat, bacteria can produce chemical compounds that kill their rivals but do not harm their own kind.

Microscopic deep-sea sulfur bacteria haven't evolved in more than two billion years— nearly half the history of Earth.

Clostridum difficile is a naturally occurring bacterium in your intestines. But too much can be fatal: *C. difficile* releases toxins that attack the intestinal lining and is often resistant to antibiotics. Doctors in Alberta, Canada, have pioneered a technique in which a patient suffering from a *C. difficile* infection is administered fecal material from family members in pill form. Fecal transplants have a 98 percent success rate.

The word *shit* comes from the Indo-European root *skheid-,* for "split, divide, separate." Another word that comes from *skheid* is science.

In 2012 researchers at MIT and Harvard discovered that photons, despite having no mass, could interact with each other and form molecules. The researchers compared the phenomenon to the lightsabers from *Star Wars*.

WTF
science

Manhattan weighs about 95 pounds more in bright sunlight than it does when cast in shadow.

If you've ever seen the man in the moon, the Virgin Mary in a grilled cheese sandwich, or the Galle Crater smiley face on the planet Mars, you're experiencing pareidolia, the psychological phenomenon that causes people to interpret random information as meaningful.

Designers use pareidolia to make androids more approachable and realistic without crossing into the "uncanny valley." First coined by Masahiro Mori in 1970, the uncanny valley occurs when we feel repulsed by something that appears familiar and lifelike but turns out to be fake—a feeling rooted in our instinct to avoid unhealthy people or anyone who just looks wrong. In other words, the uncanny valley triggers a pathogen-avoidance response.

The ability to recognize faces—and predators—was a key part of human evolution. This adaptation occurs in the fusiform gyrus, an elongated ridge in the lower part of the cerebrum's temporal lobe. Damage to this area can cause prosopagnosia, or "face blindness." Prosopagnosia can also be congenital; artist Chuck Close and neurologist Oliver Sacks were both born with face blindness.

According to a Danish study, sighted people have nightmares about 6 percent of the time, but for the blind every fourth dream is a nightmare.

———

We spend roughly 47 percent of our waking hours ignoring what's happening in the present moment.

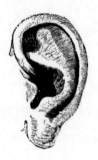

If you can't tell the difference between "Happy Birthday" and "The Star-Spangled Banner," you may have amusia, a rare disorder in which sufferers can neither perceive nor produce music.

As military men, both Che Guevara and Ulysses S. Grant knew how to carry a gun, but neither man could carry a tune. Both are believed to have suffered from amusia.

According to a Swiss study, if you lose your sense of smell you're four times more likely to die within five years than someone who hasn't.

You are more likely to die on your birthday than on any other day of the year.

———————

In a group of 23 people, there's a 50 percent chance that two individuals have the same birthday: This is called the birthday paradox. With 32 teams of 23 players apiece, the World Cup is a perfect data set to test this phenomenon. In the 2014 World Cup, as expected, 16 of the 32 sides had at least one birthday pairing, and some of the pairs even celebrated their birthdays during the tournament.

Your friends have more friends than you do. They are also wealthier and happier. And your sexual partners have had more partners than you've had. This is called the friendship paradox.

Pi is an irrational number—it cannot be reduced to a simple fraction of two integers— and its decimal place goes on forever without repeating. Theoretically, you can find your birthday, Social Security number, even a binary representation of your DNA somewhere in pi's sequence.

COFFEE AND PI. *May I have a large container of coffee? Thank you!* is a mnemonic device to remember the universe's favorite irrational number. The number of letters in each word corresponds with the first 10 digits of pi: 3.141592653.

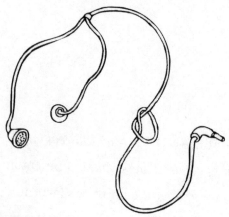

Mathematical knot theory has identified more than 100 kinds of knots that form in your pocket—so the next time you pull out your ear buds, marvel at the knot instead of getting angry: There's a high probability you've never seen it before.

According to a team of mathematicians led by Mikael Vejdemo-Johansson, there are 177,147 ways to tie your tie. With 251 workdays in a year, you could work for 705 years and never tie your tie the same way twice.

Nomadic herders in Central Asia about 3,000 years ago were the first to wear pants. Pants provided protection during mounted warfare and horseback journeys.

The 5,300-year-old Ötzi the Iceman wore a three-piece combination of loincloth and individual leggings covering just the thigh and calf.

––––––––––

Ötzi the Iceman's full genome was published in 2012. When scientists analyzed DNA samples taken from 3,700 blood donors in the Tyrol region of Austria, they discovered 19 direct descendants who all shared a particular gene mutation.

PENGUINS ARE SO SWEET! And yet, they can't taste it. Scientists have recently discovered that penguins taste only sour and salty.

Eating a polar bear's liver, loaded as it is with a lethal dose of Vitamin A, will kill you. (It will also kill the polar bear.)

The baculum is the penis bone found above the male urethra in mammals such as raccoons, chimpanzees, and polar bears. The female equivalent is the baubellum, located in the clitoris.

———

Chemical pollutants are causing polar bear penis bones to snap. PCBs (polychlorinated biphenyls), synthetic organic compounds used commercially as coolants and insulating fluids, were banned worldwide in 2001. But they still show up in high concentrations in the Arctic.

WTF
science

Humans used to have penis bones. Biologist Richard Dawkins speculates that the human penis evolved to stiffen using only hydraulic pressure so that females could better identify a strapping mate.

At 35,814 feet below the surface, the Pacific Ocean's Mariana Trench is more than a mile deeper than Mount Everest is tall. It would take a 16-pound shot about 36 minutes to fall to the bottom of the Mariana Trench.

In 1976 Richard Dawkins coined *meme* as a unit of cultural evolution, just as a gene is the unit of genetic evolution. He claims that memes, like genes, evolve through natural selection. Legal scholar Steven Wise claims the idea of memes is itself a meme.

Penguins are so sweet! And yet, they can't taste it. Scientists have recently discovered that penguins taste only sour and salty.

The 5,300-year-old Ötzi the Iceman wore a three-piece combination of loincloth and individual leggings covering just the thigh and calf.

———————

Ötzi the Iceman's full genome was published in 2012. When scientists analyzed DNA samples taken from 3,700 blood donors in the Tyrol region of Austria, they discovered 19 direct descendants who all shared a particular gene mutation.

Eating a polar bear's liver, loaded as it is with a lethal dose of Vitamin A, will kill you. (It will also kill the polar bear.)

The baculum is the penis bone found above the male urethra in mammals such as raccoons, chimpanzees, and polar bears. The female equivalent is the baubellum, located in the clitoris.

Chemical pollutants are causing polar bear penis bones to snap. PCBs (polychlorinated biphenyls), synthetic organic compounds used commercially as coolants and insulating fluids, were banned worldwide in 2001. But they still show up in high concentrations in the Arctic.

Humans used to have penis bones. Biologist Richard Dawkins speculates that the human penis evolved to stiffen using only hydraulic pressure so that females could better identify a strapping mate.

JOURNEY THROUGH THE CENTER OF THE EARTH. Imagine a tunnel drilled through Earth. With no wind resistance, it would take you 42 minutes to fall from one end of the tunnel to the other. At the center, you'd experience zero gravity and terminal velocity of 18,000 mph (Mach 23). If you factor wind resistance back in, your terminal velocity would be around 125 mph and the journey would take two and a half days.

U.S. Air Force Colonel John Paul Stapp holds the record for horizontal g-force. Accelerating backward, Stapp endured an "eyeballs out" force of 46.2 g and sustained temporary damage to his vision.

———

A woodpecker undergoes a force of 1,000 g every time it drives its beak into bark.

Psychotria elata is a flowering tree found in the tropical rain forests of Central and South America. It is commonly referred to as Hooker's Lips or the Hot Lips plant because its waxy bracts resemble two luscious red lips. Bracts are modified or specialized leaves associated with the reproductive structure of the plant. In the case of *Psychotria elata*, the labium-shaped bracts attract pollinators like hummingbirds and butterflies.

The Brazilian wandering spider is one of the world's most venomous. Although its fangs have evolved to attack small prey, this spider has been known to bite humans. Its venom can kill you—or cause a very painful and long-lasting erection.

S ix-spot burnets, *Zygaena filipendulae,* are beautiful day-flying moths with six crimson-red spots on their forewings to warn predators. When injured, the moths release cyanide. In courtship, however, males convert some of this toxin into a pheromone and crop-dust approaching females with their poisonous love cloud.

The geographic cone snail (*Conus geographus*) is one of the most venomous creatures on Earth. Like most animals living among coral reefs, it relies on chemical weapons to catch its prey. It releases a toxic form of insulin strong enough to stun whole schools of fish into hypoglycemic shock. Then it's like shooting fish in a barrel: The cone snail fires its harpoonlike tooth and reels in its stupefied prey.

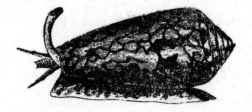

Cone snail toxin is up to a thousand times more powerful than morphine and can be used to treat certain kinds of chronic pain.

The peacock mantis shrimp is nature's greatest knockout artist. It uses a pair of specialized forelimbs, called raptorial appendages, to smash the shells of crabs, mollusks, and even the skulls of small fish. The raptorial appendages use muscle mechanics, elastic energy storage, and a linkage mechanism to accelerate a punch that is as fast as a .22 caliber bullet— about 50 times faster than the blink of a human eye.

PEACOCK SPIDERS CAN BEATBOX.

As part of its mating ritual, the male peacock spider waves a brightly colored appendage called a fan, similar to a peacock's fanned tail feathers, then vibrates his body to create a unique beat. The female feels the vibrations of the male's dance through sense organs on her legs.

The male *Nephilengys malabrensis* spider snaps off his penis inside the female while having sex. The detached penis continues to remotely deliver sperm to the female while the male, his load now lightened by 9 percent of his body weight, experiences an 80 percent increase in stamina, which helps him fight off larger suitors. Scientists believe this eunuch-inducing adaptation developed in response to the female's penchant for coital cannibalism.

Spiderwebs have one of the strongest molecular structures on Earth; even artificial spider silk is tougher than Kevlar. But recently scientists discovered something stronger: the teeth of a conical-shelled aquatic snail called a limpet. The microscopic teeth are composed of goethite, an iron oxide mineral named after German polymath and writer Johann Wolfgang von Goethe.

A nonce word is a neologism—a newly coined word—invented for a particular occasion. Nonces are also used in cryptography: Bitcoin uses a 32-bit nonce.

———

When American physicist Murray Gell-Mann discovered the fundamental constituents of the nucleon, he wanted to call them "kworks." Then he read James Joyce's novel *Finnegans Wake* and found the word *quark,* which Joyce had used as a nonce in the phrase "Three quarks for Muster Mark."

Although Edmond Halley mapped the stars in the Southern Hemisphere, invented the diving bell and magnetic compass, and convinced Isaac Newton to write down his fundamental laws of motion, one thing he never did was discover a comet. (He did predict one's return every 75 years, however.)

Technologists predict that by the mid-2020s, 90 percent of news will be algorithmically generated—mostly without human oversight.

It was long believed that a single piece of paper, regardless of its size, could not be folded more than seven or eight times. In 2002 Britney Gallivan, then a junior in high school, folded a specially made, 4,000-foot roll of toilet paper in half an astonishing 12 times. Not only that, she derived equations demonstrating how, in order to fold anything in half, it must be pi times longer than its thickness.

If you could fold a standard sheet of 20-pound copier paper 50 times, the resulting thickness would be nearly as great as the distance between Earth and the sun.

———————

The Barbados threadsnake (*Leptotyphlops carlae*) is the smallest snake on the planet. At just four inches, it can comfortably curl up on a quarter.

Domestic cats like to snuggle up in cardboard boxes because their comfortable temperature zone is much higher than ours. While the average American family sets the thermostat to 68–72 degrees Fahrenheit, cats prefer a scorching 86–97 degrees. The insulating properties of corrugated cardboard allow the cat to preserve body heat.

If you have nerve damage in your fingers, they won't wrinkle when you get them wet. Fingers evolved to wrinkle in liquid to be better at grabbing and holding onto wet objects. The wrinkles work like the tread of a tire, channeling the water away to provide better grip.

THESE BUBBLES DON'T SCRUB. Many commercial shampoos contain sodium lauryl sulfate (SLS). While technically an emulsifying surfactant—a class of chemicals that allows oil and grease to bond with water so these substances can be washed away—SLS is used in shampoos mainly because it's an inexpensive foaming agent. Foam gives consumers the impression that something is happening, but scrubbing your scalp under running water alone will clean most of the dirt out of your hair.

The placebo effect stimulates real physiological responses in patients in cases involving pain, and it can also influence blood pressure, heart rate, and neural activity. The nocebo effect is a *negative* reaction to the administration of an inert substance or to the mere suggestion of a treatment's potential side effects.

The Dunning-Kruger effect is a cognitive bias held by people whose incompetence is so complete, it robs them of the ability to realize they're incompetent. While incompetents suffer illusory superiority, truly superior people tend to underestimate their competence.

ALONE IN THE UNIVERSE. Billions and billions of years from now, all the stars we currently see in the sky will have moved so far away they will no longer be visible to the inhabitants of Earth.

Every hour, the universe expands by a billion miles in all directions. Even still, it takes 140 million years for the universe to get just 1 percent bigger.